I-SPY

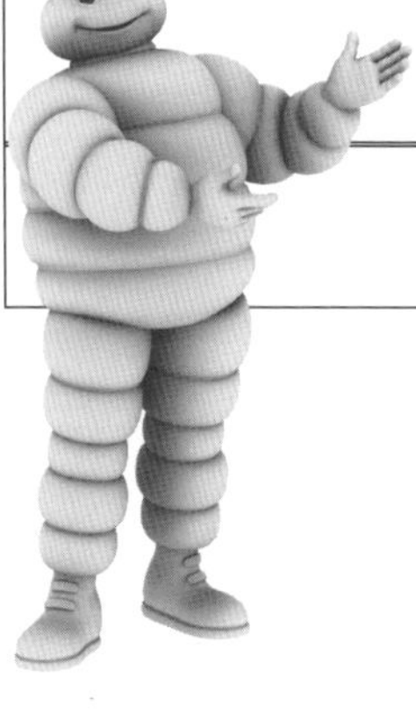

This I-SPY book belongs to:________________________

I-SPY

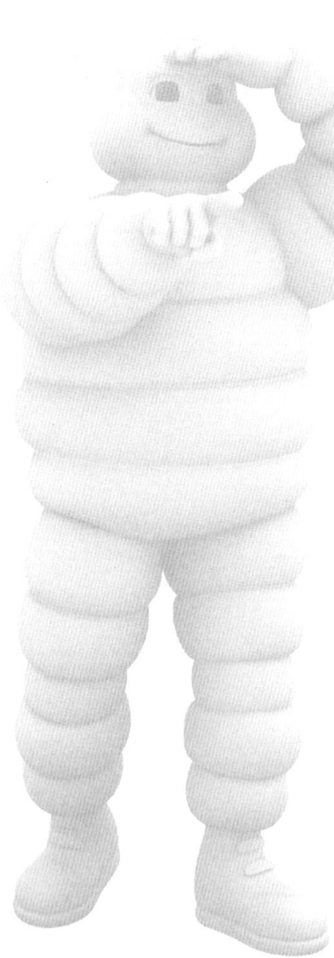

I-SPY

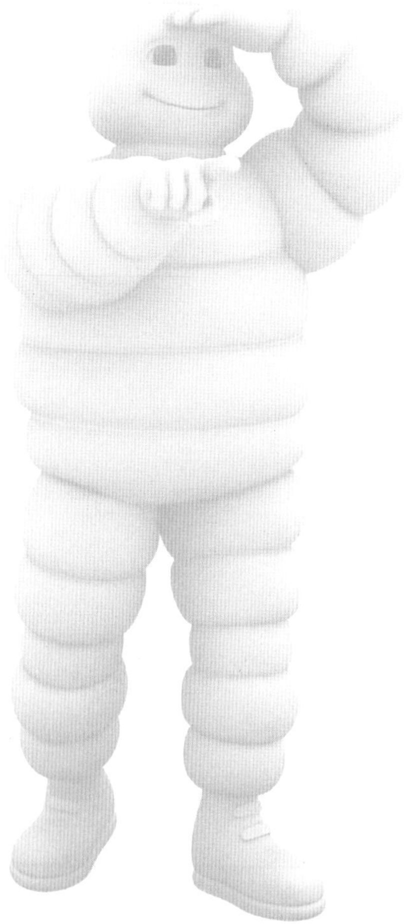

I-SPY

I-SPY

I-SPY

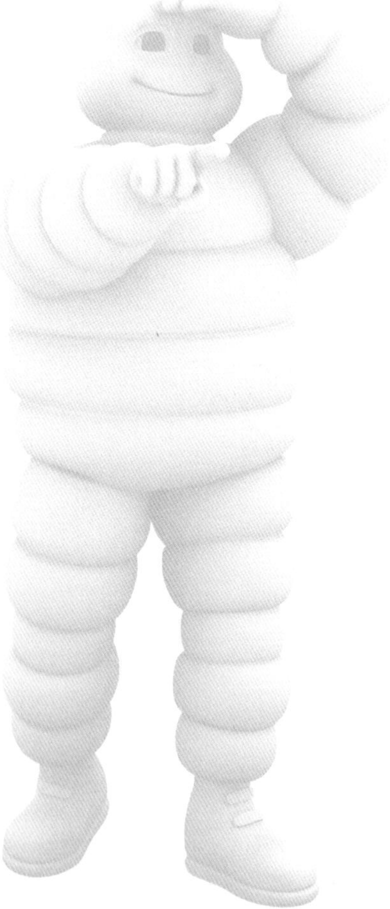

MICHELIN

I-SPY

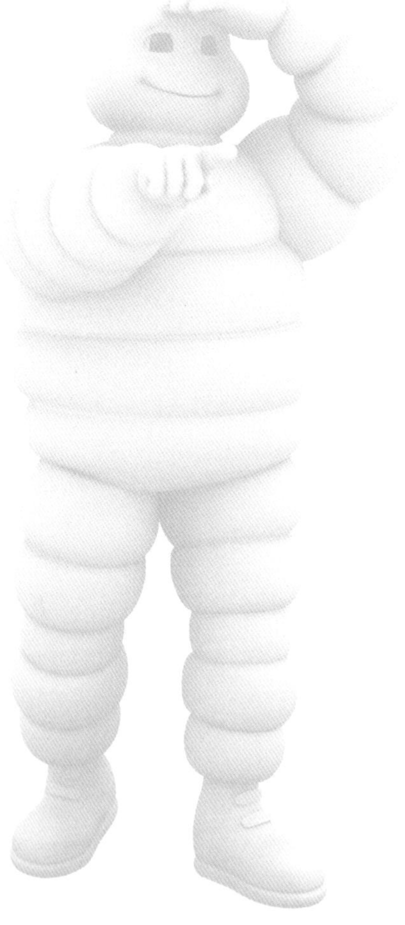

MICHELIN

I-SPY

I-SPY